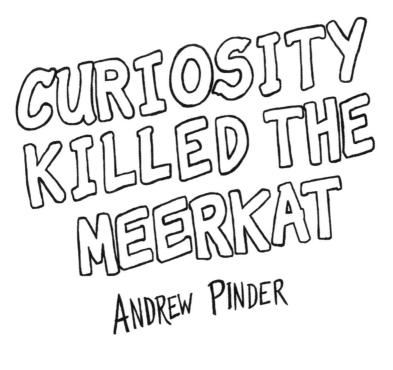

CURIOSITY KILLED THE MEERKAT

ANDREW PINDER

Virgin BOOKS

2 4 6 8 10 9 7 5 3 1

First published in Great Britain in 2012 by Virgin Books, an imprint of Ebury Publishing

A Random House Group Company

Copyright © Virgin Books 2012

www.randomhouse.co.uk

Addresses for companies within The Random House Group Limited can be found at www.randomhouse.co.uk/offices.htm

The Random House Group Limited Reg. No. 954009

A CIP catalogue record for this book is available from the British Library

The Random House Group Limited supports The Forest Stewardship Council (FSC®), the leading international forest certification organisation. Our books carrying the FSC label are printed on FSC® certified paper. FSC is the only forest certification scheme endorsed by the leading environmental organisations, including Greenpeace. Our paper procurement policy can be found at www.randomhouse.co.uk/environment

MIX
Paper from
responsible sources
FSC® C015829

Designed by www.envydesign.co.uk

Printed and bound in Italy by Graphicom srl

ISBN: 9780753541036

To buy books by your favourite authors and register for offers, visit www.randomhouse.co.uk

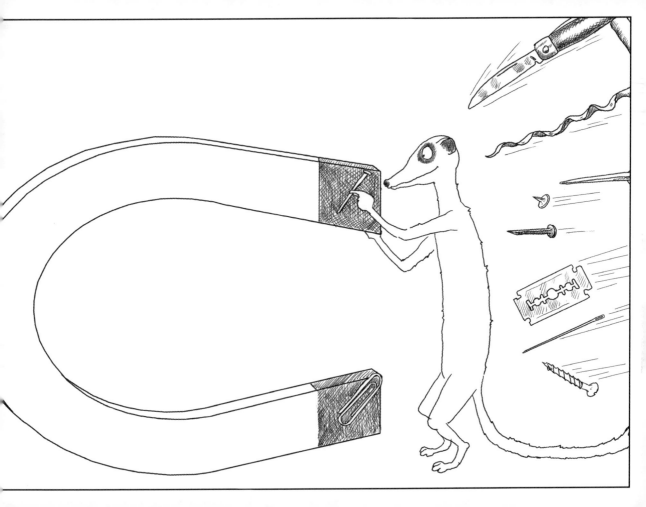

I. STUFFEM
TAXIDERMIST

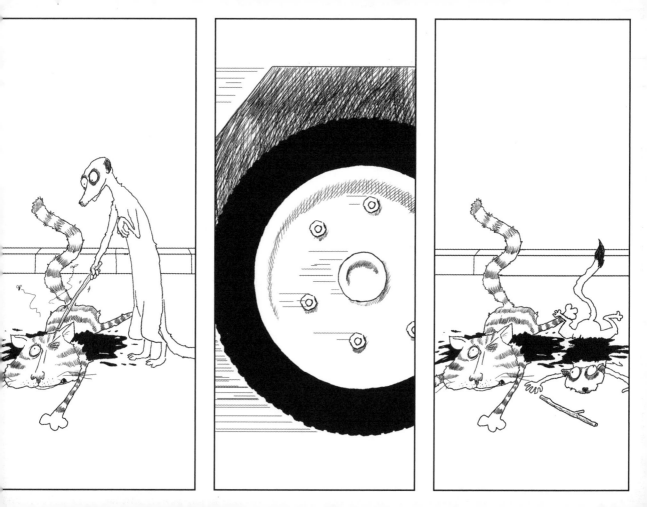

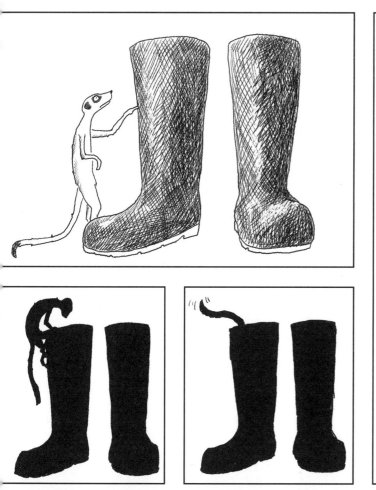

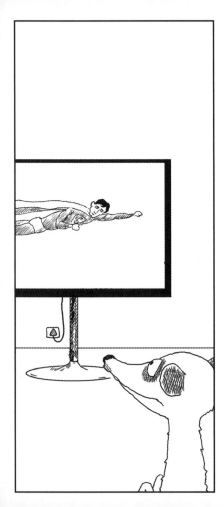

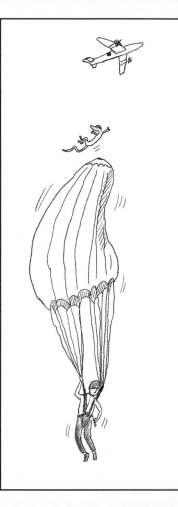

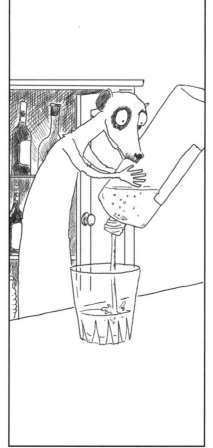

BURNITOFF
OVEN
CLEANER

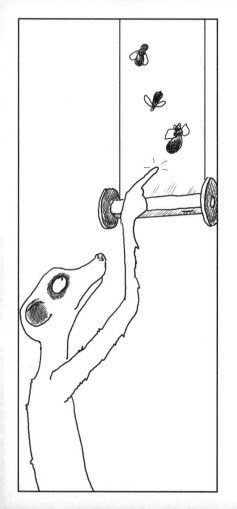
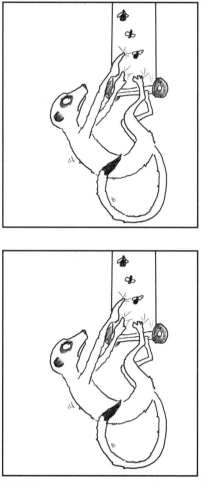
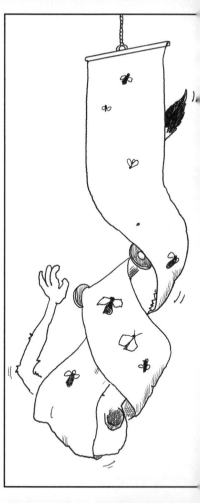

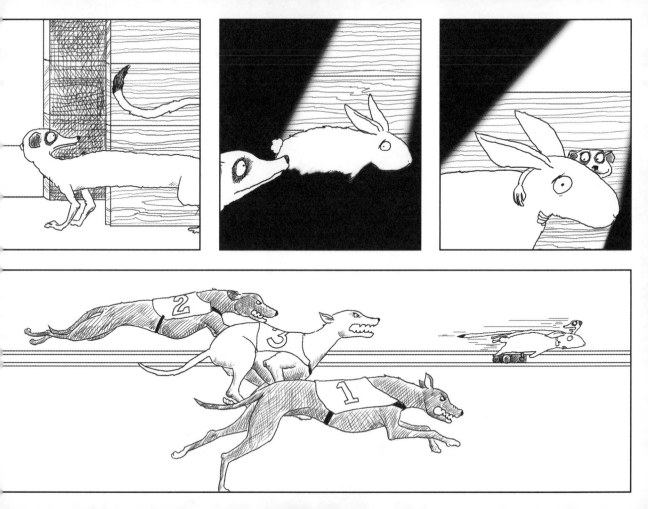

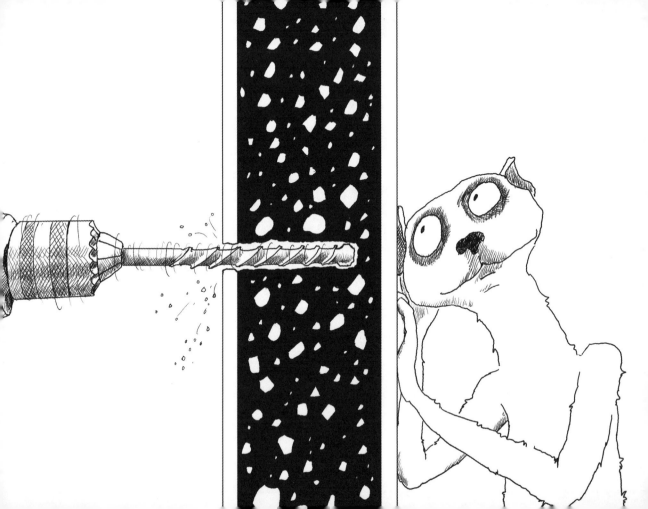

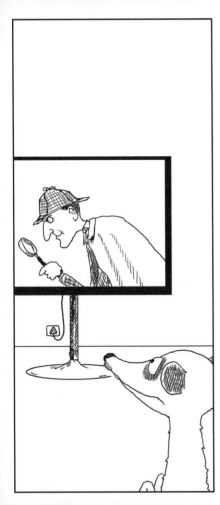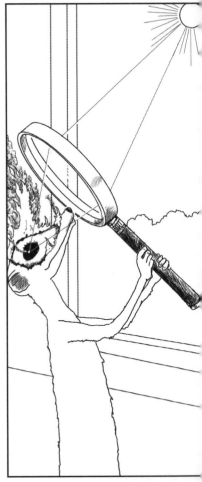

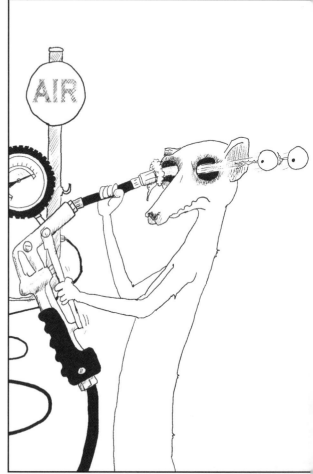

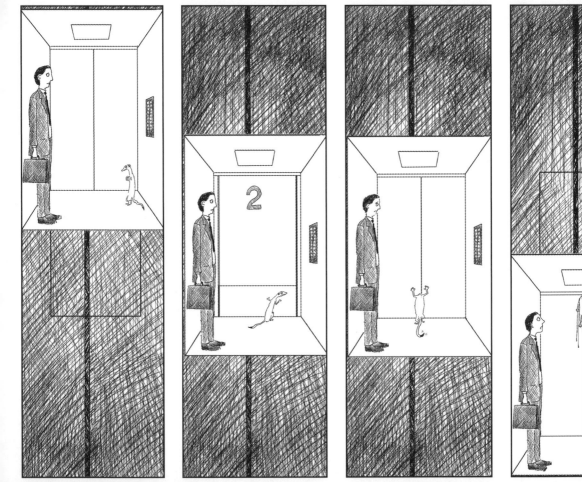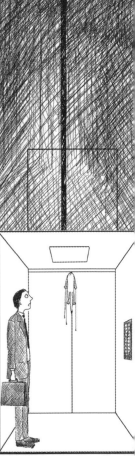

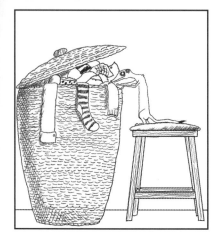

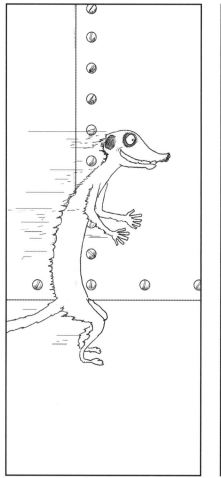

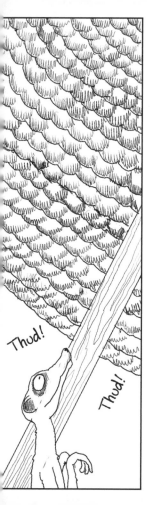

Thud!

Thud!

Thud!

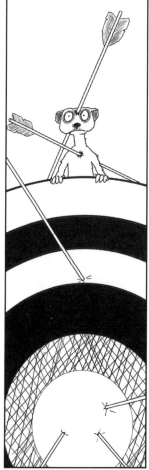

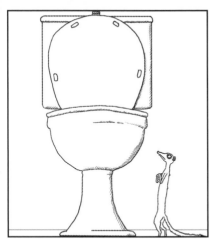
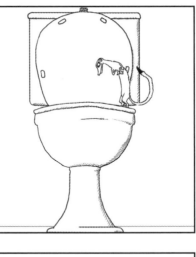
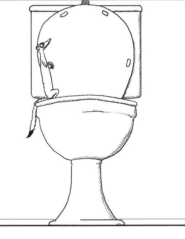

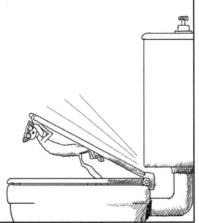

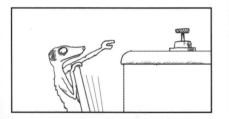

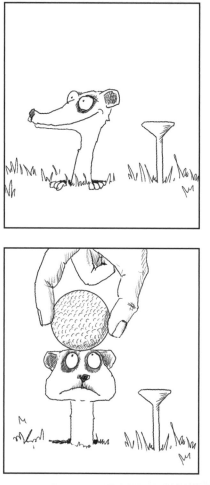

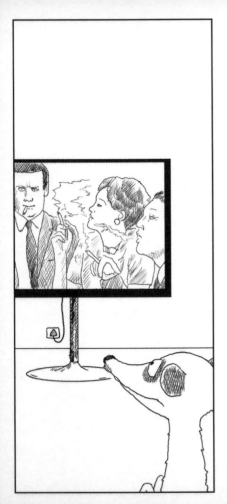
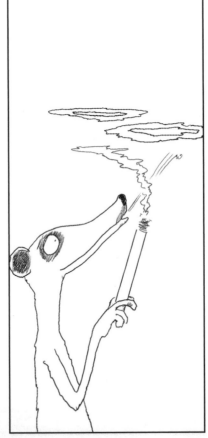
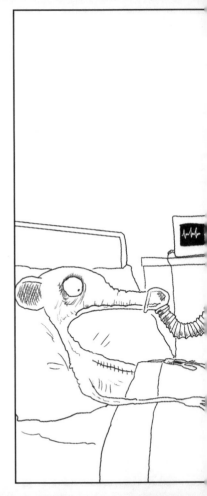

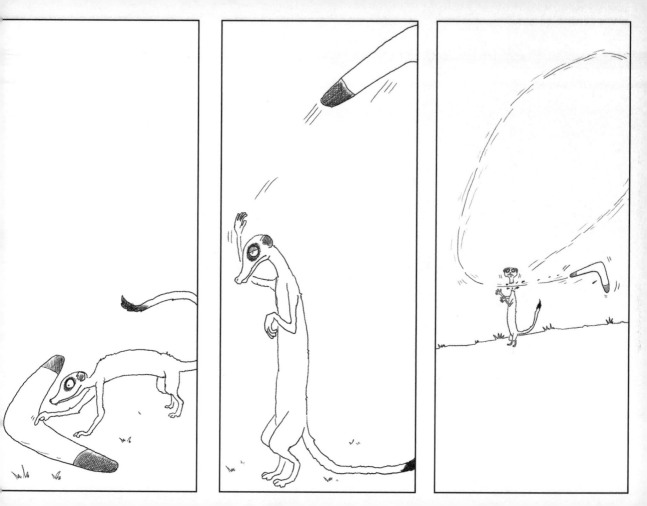

Tap, tap!

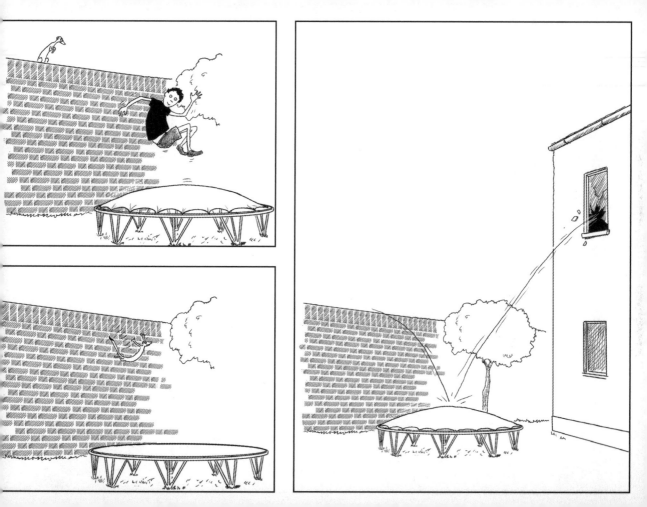

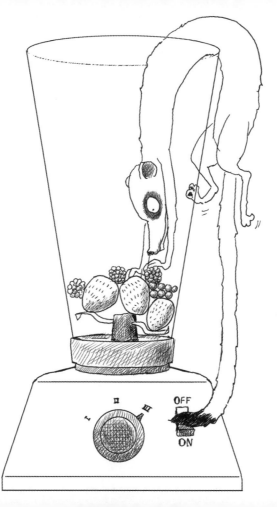

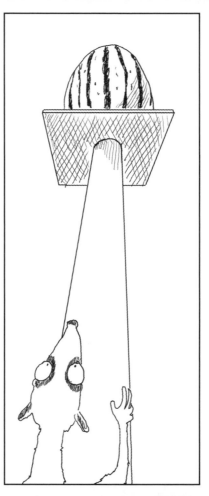

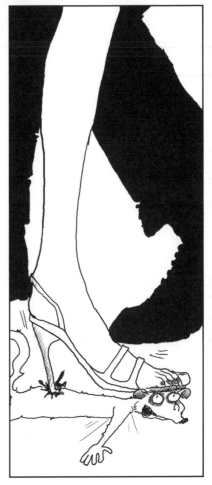

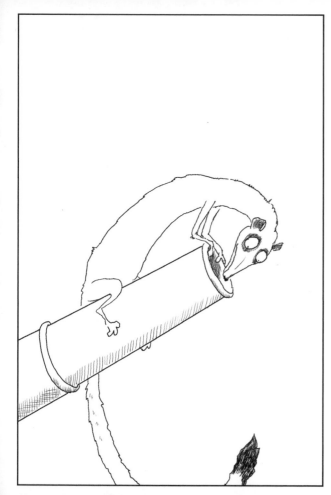

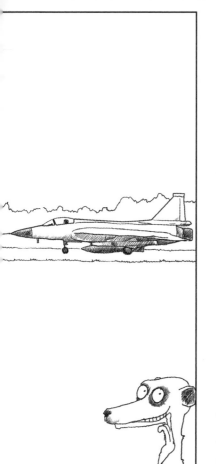

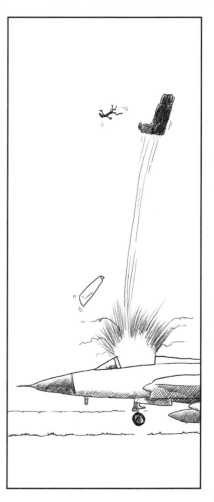

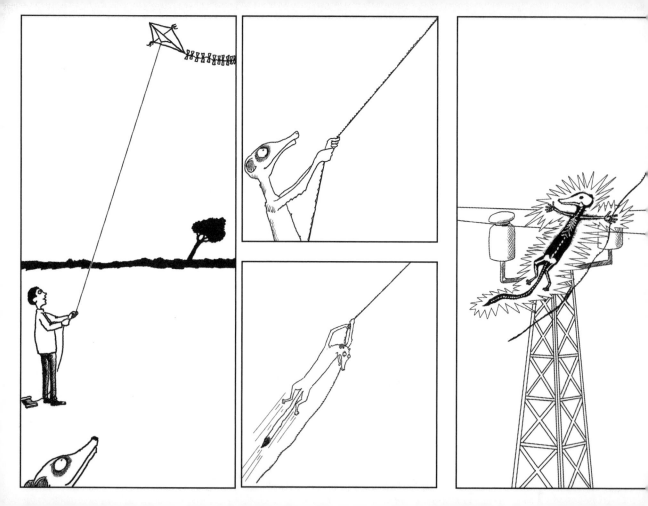

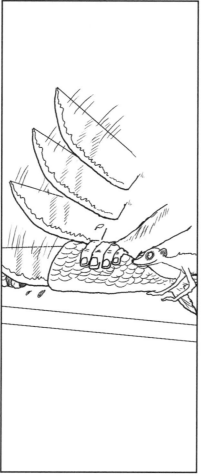

Model
Wanted

Leonardo
da Vinci

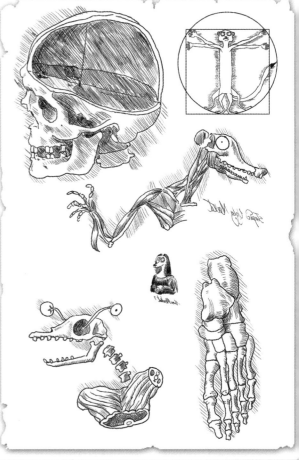

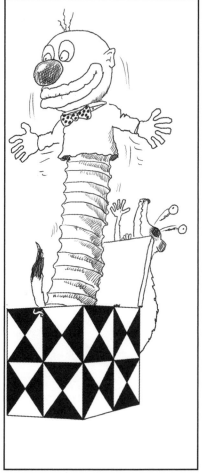

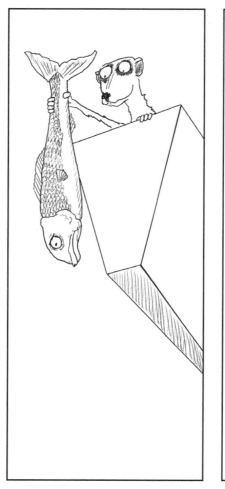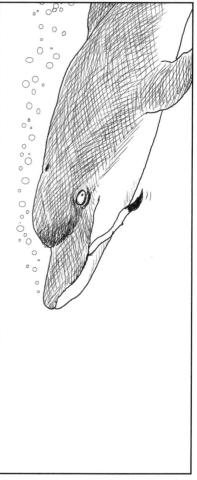

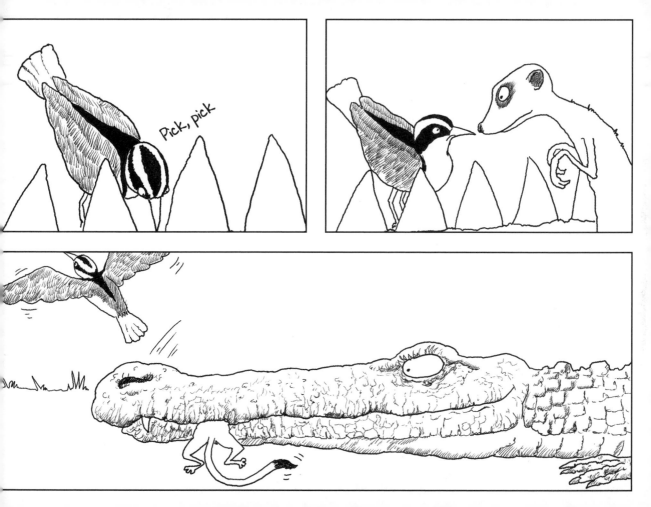

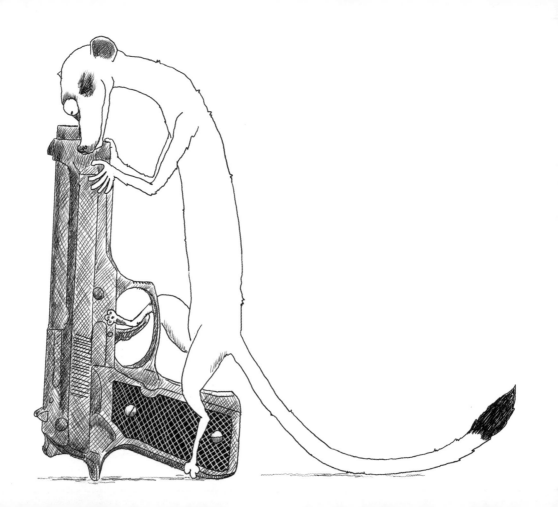

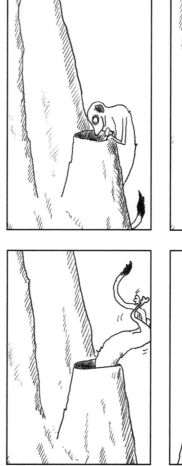

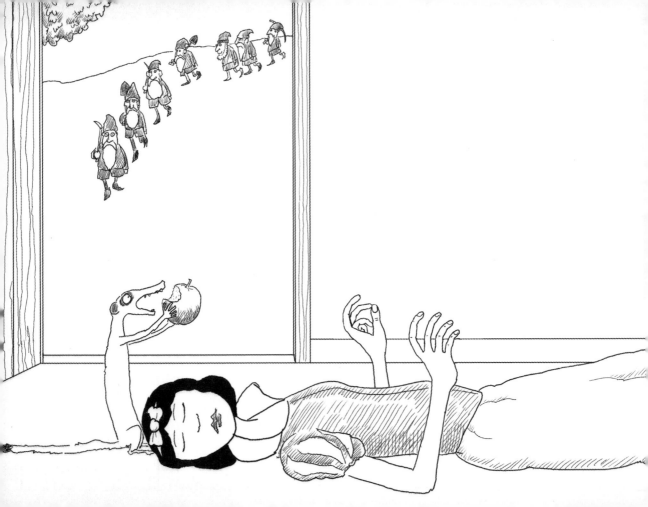

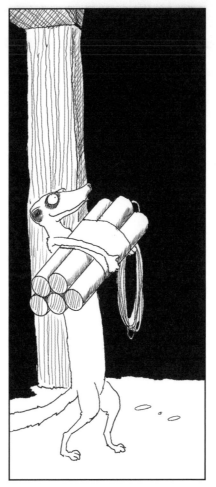

Click!

Piranhas

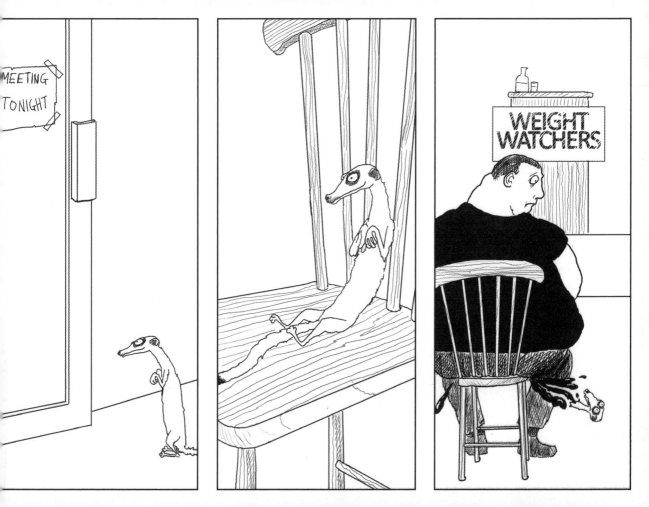

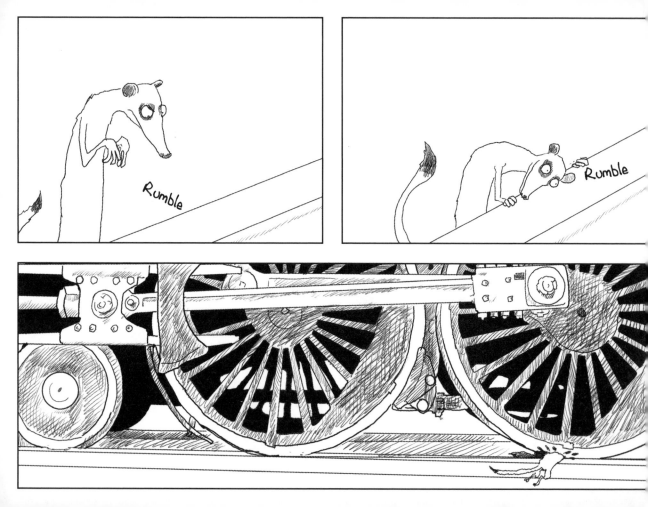